D0526802

Emily Saves the Day

Chapter 1: Off to work .... page 2

Chapter 2: The trick .... page 7

Chapter 3: The big day .... page 14

Chapter 4: Emily to the rescue! ..... page 20

Written by Emma Barnes

Illustrated by Eva Byrne

Essex County Council

3013021574982 0

Chapter 1: Off to work

My name is Emily. Until I was twelve, I lived in the country. Dad had a milk cart and I used to help him with Dobbin the horse. I helped Mum with my little brothers and sisters too. There were six of them so they were quite a handful!

On my twelfth birthday, I left school. We were poor and I needed to work. I was going to be a nursemaid and look after a rich family's children.

I had to travel to London all by myself. I'd never even been on a train before and I was nervous.

"Always wash behind your ears, Emily," Mum called from the platform. "Remember to wear your warm petticoat. Carry a handkerchief. Clean your fingernails. Eat your greens and ..."

The station guard blew his whistle.

"Goodbye everyone!" I called.

We all waved. Then I was on my own.

I was very tired when I arrived at my new home in London.

"Hello Emily," said Mrs Carrington. "This is my baby, Freddy. And the twins are Gus and Ada. I know you will adore them!"

I wasn't so sure about that. Gus and Ada had a naughty look in their eyes!

I had to sleep in the nursery with the children. My job was to look after them from morning until night. As I unpacked my things, I felt scared and lonely. What if they didn't do as I said? What would I do then?

I soon learned that Gus and Ada liked playing tricks.

They tweaked my apron strings undone.

They hid my hairbrush.

They even put a big spider on my plate when I sat down to supper!

"Eek!" I squeaked.
Gus and Ada giggled.

Then one evening, I found my missing hairbrush – inside my bed!

"Ouch!" I squeaked as it scratched my feet.

Gus and Ada chuckled from under their bed covers.

That night, I was too worried to sleep. I just had to do something about those naughty children – but what?

Chapter 2: The trick

Next day, we all did some baking. Mrs Carrington's cook showed us how to make cakes and scones. While I was giving Freddy his milk, I noticed Gus and Ada giggling. They seemed to be up to something.

Uh-oh, I thought to myself.

Flour

Salt

Later, we showed Mrs Carrington what we had made.

"Mama, Gus and I made a very special cake just for Emily," said Ada.

"How kind of the dear children!" their mother cried.

"Very kind," I agreed. "So kind, that I think Gus and Ada should have the first slice."

The twins weren't happy.

"Oh, no!" they said.

"Oh, yes," I replied.

"Of course you must, my darlings!" cried Mrs Carrington.

Ada and Gus forced down some cake. Finally they swallowed it all down.

I knew just why they didn't like it. I had seen them make that cake with salt instead of sugar! For once, their trick hadn't worked.

"No more naughty tricks?" I said when their mother was gone.

"No more tricks," the twins agreed.

After that, I was much happier. Summer came, and I took the children to the park every day. I liked patting the cart horses in the street, too. They reminded me of home.

One day on our walk, we saw something exciting was going on. There were flags everywhere. Workmen were building stands for people to sit in and hanging bunting.

They were getting ready for Queen Victoria's Diamond Jubilee. She had been queen for sixty years and there was going to be a big procession.

Mr and Mrs Carrington were sent special invitations
to sit in one of the stands.

"We want to watch the procession too!" the twins cried.

Mrs Carrington wasn't sure. "The crowds will be too big,"
she worried.

"Please, Mama, please," begged the twins.

"I'll look after them," I said. "Please let us go, Mrs Carrington."

To celebrate the Diamond Jubilee of Her Majesty's Reign

Their Royal Highnesses
The Prince and Princess of Wales

invite Mr and Mrs Carrington

Admit Bearer to seats no. A35 at the Parade

We all held our breath, waiting for her answer.

"Oh, very well," said Mrs Carrington.

"Hurrah!" cried the twins.

"Rah, rah!" squawked Freddy.

We were going to watch the Diamond Jubilee!

Chapter 3: The big day

On the big day, we got up early and put on our best clothes. I scrubbed the children's faces and brushed their hair.

The streets of London were full of people. They kept pushing and bumping us. "Stay close to me!" I told the twins. "Keep hold of the pram!"

We didn't have seats, so we needed to find a good place to watch the procession.

"How about that corner?" I said. But when I looked round, the twins had gone.

Oh no! They were up to their naughty tricks again.

"Ada! Gus!" I shouted. There was no reply.

I couldn't see the children anywhere. I began to panic, but then I had an idea. I asked a lady to watch Freddy's pram while I hitched up my skirts and climbed a tall lamp post.

I had a wonderful view above the crowds of people. I could even see Buckingham Palace! I soon spotted Ada and Gus. They were running down a side street close to the Palace itself.

I slid straight down that lamp post like a fireman down a pole!

Freddy and I soon caught up with the twins. They were staring through an open pair of tall, iron gates.

"I've a good mind to take you straight home," I told them sternly. "How dare you play tricks on me again!"

But they weren't listening. "Look!" they yelled.

The most handsome horse I'd ever seen came galloping through the gates. It paid no attention to us as it raced down the street.

What if it hurts itself? I thought. *Or somebody gets in its way?* There was no time to lose.

"After it!" I cried.

Chapter 4: Emily to the rescue!

We ran and ran through the city streets. We bumped into dustbins. We wove around milk carts. What a sight we must have been! Dogs barked at us. Old ladies stared at us. Little children waved at us. But still the runaway horse kept going.

"I'm tired," gasped Ada.

"My feet hurt," groaned Gus.

"Jump onto the pram," I cried. "We can't stop now!"

I kept running but soon my heart was pounding. My feet ached and I could hardly breathe. I had to stop. Besides, I couldn't see the horse anywhere.

"You did your best, Emily," said Ada, as we walked sadly on. It was true. But I felt disappointed, all the same.

Freddy waved his hand. "Horsey!" he said. "Neighhhhhh!"

We turned to look. Standing on the street corner was our runaway horse, calmly eating some flowers.

"Don't move!" I whispered to the twins.

The children watched as I walked towards the horse.

"Thattaboy!" I said, as it stopped munching and looked at me. It was thinking about whether to run away. I took one more careful step forward.

Then I patted the horse's neck, just like I did with Dobbin at home. The horse liked it. As it stepped towards me, I quickly grabbed its reins.

Together, the children and I took the horse back to its home.

When we got to the tall gates, lots of people came running to meet us.

"It's Sultan!" they cried. "He's back!"

A groom came to take the horse. "Thank you kindly, missy," he said to me. "We've been very worried. Without Sultan to help pull the carriage, there can't be any procession!"

"Procession?" I asked. And that's when we realised ...

This was a royal horse! The tall gates led to the stables at Buckingham Palace.

"Does this horse belong to the Queen?" I asked.

"He's the Queen's favourite," said the groom. "We were taking him to her carriage when he ran off. Come in and see."

A Palace Guard came to meet us.

"Her Majesty has asked me to thank you for what you did," he said grandly. "What is it you do?"

"I'm a servant," I replied.

"If ever you need work, there will always be a job for you at the Palace. After all, you saved the day!"

"Thank you!' I gasped.

The twins were very upset when they heard what the Palace Guard said.

"Don't leave us, Emily!" cried Ada.

"We'd miss you!" cried Gus.

"I'll stay," I told them, "if you agree to one thing. No more tricks!"

The twins promised. This time I think they really meant it.

Then we watched the
procession. And we had
the very best seats!

Emily's Family Album

Talk about the story

Answer the questions:

1　How many brothers and sisters did Emily have?

2　What tricks did Gus and Ada play on Emily?

3　What was the runaway horse called?

4　What is a 'procession'? (page 12)

5　How did Emily trick the twins after they had been baking?

6　Why did the Palace Guard tell Emily there will always be a job for her at Buckingham Palace?

7　Would you like to do Emily's job? Why or why not?

8　How was life in Victorian times different to now?

Can you retell the story in your own words?